also by William Humphrey

A Time and a Place

The Ordways

Home from the Hill

The Last Husband and Other Stories

the spawning run

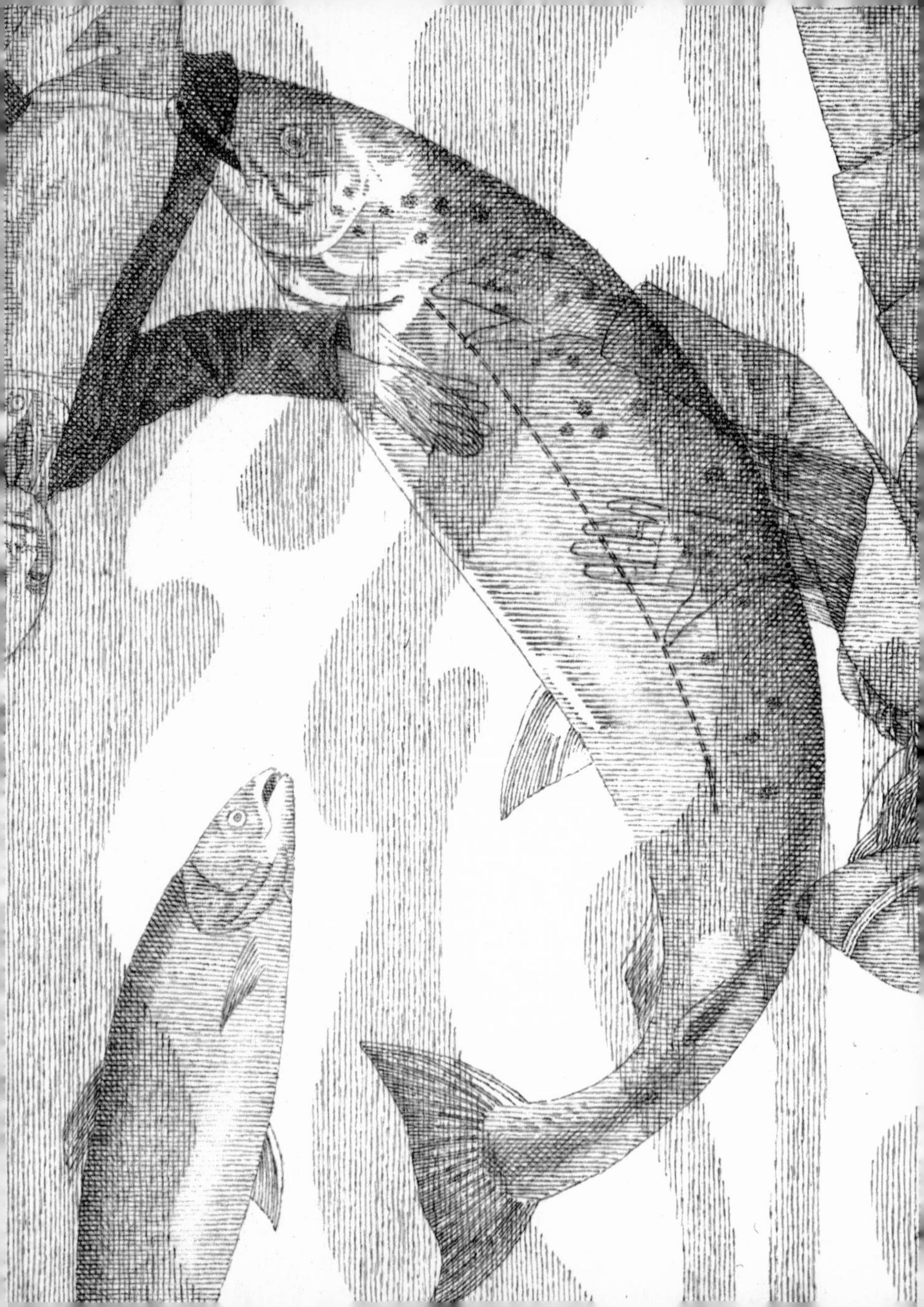

WILLIAM HUMPHREY

the spawning run

illustrated by owen wood

alfred a. knopf new york 1970

This is a Borzoi Book published by Alfred A. Knopf, Inc.

Published in the United States by Alfred A. Knopf, Inc.,
New York, and simultaneously in Canada
by Random House of Canada Limited, Toronto.
Distributed by Random House, Inc., New York.
Library of Congress Catalog Card Number: 70–127088
This work first appeared in ESQUIRE *Magazine under a different title.*
Manufactured in the United States of America *First Edition*

to dorothy

the spawning run

dorset, may 12

The Itchen, the Test, the Frome: the fabled chalk streams of south England, where Dame Juliana Berners and Isaak Walton fished—here I am in the middle of them, it's spring, the season has opened, and I'd might as well be in the Sahara. Even the Piddle, known also as the Puddle—the brook running through the farm here—holds good trout. I have seen them hanging in the shallows above the mill-race, resting from their run, reaccustoming themselves to fresh water—for these will be sea-run trout, gamest of them all, returning to spawn: broad in the shoulder, deep in the belly, spotted like the gravel of the stream bed so that at first you don't see them, only their rippling shadows on the bed. The personal property, every one of them, of Mr. "Porky" Mitchell, the meat-pie king. Eighty-five hundred pounds sterling he paid for the fishing in three miles of the stream for ten years. So Tom Mears, my landlord, tells me. I stroll over daily to watch these trout.

They congregate below the signpost which reads STRICTLY PRIVATE FISHING, just downstream from the stone bridge with the weatherworn cast-iron plaque threatening transportation to Virginia to anyone found defacing it. Mr. Mitchell's water bailiff watches me.

dorset, may 13

The Anglo-Saxons are anglers. Here on Sundays queues of them with cane poles and minnow pails line the banks of the quarter-mile of public water. In and out among their lines one of Her Majesty the Queen's swans and her cygnets glide. The serenity is seldom disturbed by anybody's catching anything.

Nowhere is the class division more sharply drawn than in the national pastime. "Fishing in Britain," says the pamphlet sent me by The British Travel and

Holiday Association, "falls into three classes: game, sea, and coarse." Read: upper, middle, and lower. Trout taken from the public water here must be returned; they are the property of Mr. Mitchell that have strayed. Only coarse fish may be kept by the coarse.

Discussed fishing with my new friends at The Pure Drop.

"Pike season don't begin for another two months, but there's some fair fishing round and about for roach, dace, tench," I'm told.

I remember reading those names of English fish in Walton, but what they are I don't know. They sound "coarse."

"I'm talking about trout," I say.

I get the look I've seen them give those who frequent the Saloon Bar, where the same beer costs tuppence ha'penny a pint more than it does here in the Public Bar. Bill Turner, speaking for them all, says, "Trout, is it? Ah well, I wouldn't know, not being a toff meself."

dorset, may 15

While watching the fish in the millrace today, I glimpsed something go through that looked like a torpedo.

dorset, may 16

Immoderate people, the British, especially in their pastimes, their reputation to the contrary notwithstanding. Take my new friend Dr., which is to say Mr., M.

M. is an authority, perhaps *the* authority, on the long-term effects of prisoner-of-war-camp diet on the male urinary system. On this important and insufficiently heeded aspect of war, M. has testified as an expert at war-crimes trials and in many veterans' disability-pension case hearings. This, however, is a study which M. has taken up only in the last few years, and which he pursues only out of fishing season. He is retired from practice.

He retired and came home from Africa to London three years ago, then moved down here, where he has the fishing on Thursdays and Fridays on a half-mile beat on the Frome, and Mondays, Tuesdays, and Wednesdays on a three-quarter-mile beat on the Piddle, sublet from Mitchell, the meat-pie king. Saturdays he plays the football pools.

I met M. in the farmyard yesterday afternoon when my wife and I came in from our bike ride over the heath. He was wearing waders and was busy rigging up a bamboo fly rod. I watched him do it. He jointed the rod, first greasing the male ferrule by rubbing it on the wing of his nose, attached the reel, drew the already greased line through the guides, attached a leader (a "cast" they call it here) with a deftly tied central draught knot, opened a fly book, and selected a fly. Holding it between thumb and forefinger he said—his first words to me—"What fly is that?"

I took it from him. I had tied the pattern. "I don't know what you may call it here; we would call that a Gold-ribbed Hare's Ear where I'm from. It's a number 14," I said.

He reached into the trunk of his car (the "boot" they say here) and took out another rod. He jointed this rod, put on a reel, threaded the line through the guides, and handed it to me.

"You'll do," he said. "Come along."

We went past the old gristmill and under the railroad trestle and across the meadow to where his beat of the river begins. A slow, flat, winding, and narrow stream the Piddle is, never more than ten or twelve feet wide, though just as deep, and choked with water weeds that twine snakily in the current. Along its banks not a tree or a bush to interfere with casting.

We fished for an hour, or rather I fished: M. sat on the bank, smoking his pipe and watching. I do not like to be watched while I fish. In fact, I cannot fish if I'm watched. Cannot even cast my fly properly. And I felt bad that he was giving up his sport, especially knowing how costly it was. He refused to fish, however. "I do it every day," he said. "I want to see you catch something." I caught nothing.

After an hour he announced that it was time for tiffin. I tried to decline half his tea, but when he said that if I did not share it with him he would eat none of it either, I said I would share it with him. So I had half of one of Mr. Mitchell's pork pies, half a cucumber sandwich, half a banana sandwich, and a cup of tea. Afterward I accepted a fill for my pipe from his tobacco pouch. While we smoked, M. told me about himself.

Upon finishing his residency in tropical medicine, he got married, went on a fishing honeymoon to Ireland, returned to London, where he set his wife up in a flat in South Kensington, and shipped out to Nairobi. There he spent the next twenty-five years, returning home on three months' leave every year to fish, and to see his wife. Once in that time he came back for an entire year. He had come into a legacy of £3000, which he spent on salmon fishing in Scotland. Best year of his life. If he should ever win a pot in the football pools, it's what he would do again. His period of service in Nairobi concluded, he came home three years ago, gave up the flat in London and brought his wife (their grown son was now out in Ottawa) down here and bought his fishing. On this beat here he had killed six so far, this early in the season, the biggest one thirty-two pounds.

"A thirty-two-pound trout!" I exclaimed.

"No, no. Not trout. Salmon."

"Salmon! In this little trickle of a stream?"

Now I know what that shape was that passed through the millrace yesterday, its dorsal fin out of water like a periscope.

This evening, telling Tom Mears about my day, I learned why M. did not fish while I was fishing. Here in England when one buys a beat on a piece of water, or subleases as M. does from the meat-pie king, one not only buys a specified number of days of the week, or half-days, one also buys a specified number of rods. What M. has is one rod for his days on his beat. Should he bring along a guest, he may not fish himself. I won't be taking up his invitation to go with him another time. In fact, I must give up hope of fishing in Britain. It's too complicated.

dorset, may 17

So much for yesterday's resolution! I was at my desk this morning when I heard Tom call up from below, "Bill? Come down! Something here I think you'll want to see."

On the bricks of the back court, at the feet of a man in waders, lay the biggest fish I have ever seen. Silver, sleek, shaped like the fuselage of a jet plane. Its jaws were bared in a ferocious snarl. I had never seen one, but I recognized it.

"Yes, that's a right nice cock salmon. Should run

to about forty pounds, maybe forty-five," said the man in waders.

I stretched myself out on the bricks beside the fish. We were just about a match.

And from there I lay looking up at Mr. Porky Mitchell with envy and class hatred.

dorset, may 19

"Scotland," said Tom. "There's the place for you. Up there they've got fishing hotels where you can buy rights by the day or by the week."

"Too far. Too expensive."

"Wales, then. Be there by afternoon."

Wales. . . . The Severn. The Wye. The Usk. . . .

In the county town of Dorchester—Thomas Hardy's Casterbridge—where I went today to get myself outfitted with fishing tackle, I parked my car in the municipal lot.

"Enjoying your holiday over here, are you, sir?" asked the attendant as he copied onto my ticket the number of my Virginia license plate.

"Very much, thank you."

"First visit to Dorchester? Perhaps I can tell you some of the sights to see."

"Very kind of you. As a matter of fact, I've been here before."

"What! Here to Dorchester?"

"Why, yes."

"What would ever bring you back a second time?"

"Well, what has brought me back several times is my interest in your great man, Hardy."

"Mr. Hardy, is it? I knew him well. I was his driver."

"His driver! Were you really? You fascinate me!"

"Do I then? Well, so I was! Yes, Mr. Hardy had one of the very earliest automobiles in Dorchester. A fine big Daimler it was, the kind they don't make anymore. I used to run him up to London every month. We did it always in under three hours. Loved speed, he did."

"Loved speed? Now I should never have expected that!" (He used to get about the town on a tricycle.)

" 'George, faster!' he would say. 'George' (that's me) 'faster!' Ah, he was a fine man, and when he died he remembered me in his testament. I keep a photo of him here in the hut."

"Do you! Well, that is wonderful! You must cherish a very tender memory of him."

"I do. I do. Be glad to show it to you, if you'd care to see it."

"I'd love to see it!"

The photograph—framed—bore only a faint resemblance to Hardy. I said, "This doesn't look much like other portraits of him I have seen."

"Oh, you're wrong there, sir. I knew him well and that's caught him, all right. A speaking likeness, that. Yes, yes. Built some of the very finest houses in this town, did Mr. Hardy."

I knew that Hardy had spent a long apprenticeship as an architect, but it seemed hardly the thing to remember him for. "What's more important," I said, "he wrote some of the best novels and some of the most beautiful poems in the language."

"That will be the brother," said the parking-lot attendant. "It's Mr. *Henry* Hardy we're speaking of, the building contractor. Ah, he was a fine man, and it's a pleasure to talk to you about him."

My tackle consists of my rod: a two-handed ten-foot second-hand Farlow which looks as if it has caught a great many fish; line: oiled silk, torpedo-head taper, FBG; two hundred feet of backing, thirty-pound test; reel; hobnailed hip boots; two dozen gaudy big double-hooked salmon flies; gaff; two books on the salmon, his habits, and how to catch him. Or rather, no. One does not catch a salmon. One kills a salmon. The distinction resembles that preserved in English between the verbs "to murder" and "to assassinate": ordinary citizens are murdered, leaders are assassinated. So with the King of Fish. He is not caught, like your perch or your pike or your lowly pickerel. He is killed.

Mr. Porky Mitchell's peculiar word is now explained: salmon, male and female, are called cocks and hens, I learn from my books. The salmon appears to be a very odd fish.

ross-on-wye, may 21

In the spring a salmon's fancy also turns to thoughts of love. Not a young salmon's but an old salmon's. And not lightly. With the single-mindedness of a sailor returning home after a four-year cruise without shore leave.

The salmon is anadromous. That is to say, he

leads a double life, one of them in freshwater, the other in saltwater. His freshwater life may be said to be his private, or love life; his saltwater life his ordinary, or workaday life. The salmon reverses the common order of human affairs: a lot is known about his private life but nothing at all about the rest. We get the chance to study him only when the salmon is making love. For when the salmon, aged two, and called at that stage a parr, leaves his native river and goes to sea (to be a smolt until he returns to spawn, whereupon he becomes a grilse), nobody, not even Professor Jones, D. Sc., Ph.D., Senior Lecturer in Zoology, University of Liverpool, whose book *The Salmon* I am reading, knows where he goes or how he lives, whether in the sea he shoals together with his kind or goes his separate way, why some stay there longer than others or why some return home in the spring and others not until the autumn. He disappears into the unfished regions, or the unfished depths, or both, of the ocean, and is not seen again until—it may be as little as one year or as much as four years later—impelled by the spawning urge, he reenters the coastal waters and the estuaries and up the rivers to his native stream like some missing person returning after an absence of years from home.

Nothing of what the salmon does in the sea is known, only what he does not do: namely, reproduce himself. He cannot. For his mating and for the incubation of his offspring, fast-flowing freshwater is required. And he can't, or won't, or at least would a lot rather not spawn in any but the same stream in which he himself was spawned. This may be far inland, perhaps deep in the mountains of Wales, and he, when he begins to feel the urge, may be in the Baltic Sea—in tagging experiments salmon have been tracked as far as sixteen hundred miles from their native streams. No matter—home he heads, and, what is even more remarkable, he knows how to find his way back. He does it, they think, by smell.

By 1653, when Walton published *The Compleat*

Angler, tagging experiments had already shown that salmon, if they can, return to their native rivers to spawn. Walton writes,

> Much of this has been observed by tying a *Ribband* or some known *tape* or *thred* in the tail of some young *Salmons,* which have been taken in Weirs as they swimm'd toward the salt water, and then by taking a part of them again with the known mark at the same place at their return from the Sea . . . and the like experiment hath been tryed upon young *Swallowes,* who have after six moneths absence, been observed to return to the same chimney, there make their nests and habitations for the Summer following: which has inclined many to think, that every *Salmon* usually returns to the same river in which it was bred, as young *Pigeons* taken out of the same *Dove-cote,* have also been observed to do.

Since Walton's time, much thought and many ingenious experiments have sought answers to the questions, why and how the salmon does this. Memory? Instinct? The "conclusion" of these, up to now, is Professor Jones's hypothesis that each river has its characteristic odor, and that throughout the period of his wanderings in the sea the salmon retains a memory of, one may say a nostalgia for, this odor. Neither Professor Jones nor anybody else knows how the salmon finds and follows the trail of this scent through hundreds and hundreds of miles of salt seawater. This smell Professor Jones supposes to be a complex one, composed of many things, chemical and physical, owing to the different substances dissolved in the water, and it is this complexity which makes the scent of each river unique and unmistakable to its salmon offspring. One is asked to imagine the salmon working his way home past tributaries where the scent is almost but not quite the one he is seeking, like the hero of Proust's *Remembrance of Things Past* almost succeeding but repeatedly just failing to recapture the sense of happiness that came to him momentarily with the taste of the *petite madeleine* dipped in tea, until finally the flavor reminds of when he last tasted it and his mind is flooded with recollections of his childhood vacations at his Aunt Léonie's house in Combray.

Salmon do have a very fine sense of smell. Migrant salmon on their way upstream have been seen to shy and scatter when a bear put its paw in the water above them. Also when a very dilute solution of the odor of the human skin was put in the water above them. And they do not respond this way when the odor introduced into the water is not one they associate with one or another of their natural enemies. So their sense of smell is not only sharp, it is highly discriminating as well.

Say that he is *my* salmon, the one I am hoping to catch—kill, that is—a native of the parts I am headed for, a salmon of the River Teme, in mid-Wales. Through the sea he will have swum at speeds—this too established by tagging experiments—of up to sixty-two miles per day. He will have come, as I have just done, up the Bristol Channel.

Off Cardiff he will have gotten his first whiff of fresh water; there the River Taff empties into the Channel, and there he will have rested for some days or even weeks, not from exhaustion, but because too sudden a change from salt water to fresh brings on a shock that can be fatal to him. Then past the Usk on his left, the Bristol Avon on his right, both redolent of the scent he is seeking, but neither just quite the thing itself. At Aust Ferry instead of the Wye he will have known to take the Severn, and to keep on it, ignoring hundreds of tributaries large and small, until just below Worcester, coming in from the left, is that waft which to him is like none other in the world.

The average salmon lives seven years. Thus a year in a salmon's life equals ten years in a man's life. Suppose a man left home at twenty and was gone for forty years, wandering as far as sixteen hundred miles away, and then at sixty he walked back without a map and with nobody along the way to ask directions of, no signposts to guide him, no landmarks: this would be about comparable to the salmon's feat in finding his way back to his native river to spawn. Add obstacles in his path in the form of falls as much as twelve feet high, not to be bypassed, to have to leap.

The salmon is named for his salient characteristic. *Salmo,* from the Latin, means "the leaper," and comes (as does the word salient, by the way) from the verb *salire,* to leap. People came and watched and wondered at the salmon leaping in Walton's time, and they still do. "Next, I shall tell you," Walton writes,

> that though they make very hard shift to get out of the fresh Rivers into the Sea, yet they will make harder shift to get out of the salt into the fresh Rivers, to spawn or possesse the pleasures that they have formerly found in them, to which end they will force themselves through *Flood-gates,* or over *Weires,* or *hedges,* or *stops* in the water, even beyond common belief. *Gesner* speaks of such

places, as are known to be above eight feet high above the water. And our *Cambden* mentions (in his *Brittannia*), the like wonder to be in *Pembrokeshire,* where the river *Tivy* falls into the Sea, and that the fall is so downright, and so high, that the people stand and wonder at the strength and slight that they see the *Salmon* use to get out of the Sea into the said River; and the manner and height of the place is so notable, that it is known far by the name of *Salmon-leap.*

At a pool in Ross-shire, according to Professor Jones, salmon have been seen making a leap of eleven feet four inches vertical, and he calculates that to do this the fish must have been moving at a vertical speed of twenty miles an hour as they left the water at the foot of the falls. We saw nothing so spectacular as that; but we joined a small crowd of people gathered on the bank of a river this afternoon and watched salmon leaping a falls about six feet high, and their determination and their strength and their grace, their hardihood even, as they hurled themselves at what seemed an insurmountable obstacle, some of them repeatedly falling back as time after time they just failed to clear the top, drew cheers from all of us who saw it.

It may live as long as nine months more while spawning, but the moment it re-enters freshwater the salmon has eaten its last bite.

wales, may 22

Salmon fishing, Professor Jones—himself no angler, he tells us—observes, is a sport for the well-to-do. While my wife went inside to check us into the hotel I insinuated my VW between two new Bentleys parked in the court. An incensed peacock was pecking at himself in the hubcap of one of the Bentleys with brainless persistency. Each peck drew from his beak a dash of his spittle. When he had obliterated with his spittle the rival in that hubcap he spread his tail proudly and went strutting to attack another Bentley hubcap, passing up those of my VW with lordly disdain.

This hotel of ours, patronized by Bentley owners, with peacocks to decorate its stately lawns, winding, as the brochure puts it, among the lovely valley of the Teme, surrounded by thirty-five acres of parkland and enchanting gardens, is a nineteenth-century reproduction of a fourteenth-century Italian villa, with loggias and campanili, called The Redd. That is not a Welsh word, nor, as one might think after driving, as we did today, through Fforest Fawr, a quaint old spelling of red. One who is up on his salmon lore, as I am fast becoming, knows that a redd is a salmon's nest.

"They won't be biting tomorrow," said my wife on her return.

"What?"

"The fish. Won't be biting tomorrow."

"How do you come to know that?"

"Learned it the first thing. Old gentleman just inside the door was banging a barometer on the wall. Seeing me he burst into a broad frown and said, 'They won't be biting tomorrow.' So that's the outlook, my friend."

"Fellow guest?"

"A sample. Others coming out of the woodwork. This is going to be fun."

"Fishing," said mine host, Mr. Osborne, "is with artificial fly, strictly."

It may be that he says the same thing in the same tone to his British guests as well, but I thought I detected a pointedness in the way he said it to me. Turning inside out the pockets of my chinos, "Haven't got a worm on me," I said. Mr. Osborne was not amused. Maybe not convinced.

We stood on the flagged terrace overlooking the valley a hundred and fifty feet below, the top of a great pine tree level with our eyes. Below us spread a meadow of vivid green, its pile as regular as wall-to-wall carpeting, grazed by a herd of red Hereford cattle. At four o'clock in the afternoon the river was shadowed by the mountain rising directly behind it. Small pastures and hangers of dark trees dotted the mountainside, and scattered small gray stone farm-houses, low to the ground.

"Still time to have a try at it if you'd like," said Mr. Osborne. "On the house. Go down and have a look at the big pool just there. That was Major Butler's beat today, but he's come in already, having killed a twenty-seven-pound cock. There's more where that one came from."

I went down through the enchanting garden. The rhododendrons, laid out in a maze and growing twelve feet tall, were in full bloom and murmurous with bees. The garden path ended at a five-barred gate. Attached to its right-hand post and swinging at a right angle to the bars was a low hinged gate at the top of the long flight of wooden steps leading down to the water. A woman in a tweed suit and wearing a felt hat stood at this gate, her back to me, watching something below so intently that I had to hem and then hem again and finally to say, "Excuse me, please." She turned then, slowly, not startled, for it was plain that she had heard all my little signals, and gave me a smoldering look. I am writing this before going to bed, but it is not because of what came later that I say it: her look was smoldering. She was deep in reverie. And yet she was quite aware of me. Aware of and quite indifferent to me, even disdainful of me, and, far from embarrassed and trying to hide the mood I had surprised her in, she seemed to flaunt it before me. I have seen such a look in women's eyes before, both hot and haughty —newlyweds often have it: *I have been aroused, yes, but I've got my man, I'm not for you.* Now, however, I am perhaps letting myself be influenced by what came later.

Halfway down the steps I met a man coming up. We brushed in passing, so narrow was the way. But I did not see his face nor think to return his

"Good afternoon" to me until it was too late, still burning as I was from the woman's look.

Above the pool the water was fast and broken, but at the pool it broadened and deepened and flattened out. Above the still surface of the pool hovered a mist of mayflies performing their nuptial flight, rising and dipping like swallows at evening, the females dropping to the surface for an instant to deposit their eggs, others, their mating and with it their brief lives over, falling spent to the water on outspread wings. The faint, barely audible sound, as of a bubble bursting, which a dimpling trout makes as it sucks in a fly, was multiplied so many times it sounded as though the pool were at a slow boil. Then as I watched, trout, mostly small, began to leap for the hovering flies, rising straight out into the air and straining upright on their tails on the surface of the water like trained puppies begging. Then I heard a wallop and a heavy splash and out of the corner of my eye saw spray and then saw rings rippling outward in widening circles that rapidly covered the entire pool from bank to bank. I took the steps up three at a time and, flinging open the gate, nearly hit in the back the man I had met coming down. He was talking to the woman. Neither of them took notice of me.

On the way downstairs in the hotel, rod, gaff, fly book in hand, I met my wife.

"How does it look?" she asked.

"Scary. There's one old sockdolager in there that if I should hook him is liable to pull me in and chomp off a leg."

"I'll come along and protect you," she said.

"Come on then! Because they're not going to be biting tomorrow."

We went back down the path toward the gate. Nearing it, I saw something that made me take my wife's elbow and steer her aside and hustle her down an alley of rhododendrons until we got where I felt I could safely speak. I said, "Go quietly out there and look down that way and come back and tell me if you see what I think I just saw."

When she finally tore herself away and came back to me, my wife said, "If I hadn't seen it for myself——"

"I still don't," I said.

But another look convinced me.

"Right up there against that gate," I said to my wife. "In public. In broad daylight."

"Not fifty yards from the hotel," said my wife. "All rooms booked."

"Standing up," I said. "Fully clothed."

"I don't believe it either," said my wife. "I'd better take another look to convince myself."

"You've looked your fill already," I said.

"Do you suppose," said she, "that they're married?"

"To each other, do you mean?"

"Can we get back to the house that way around the bushes?"

"We're not going back to the house."

"What are we going to do, watch?"

"Wait."

So, me thinking of all those fish on the rise and especially of the one that had made that mighty wallop, those tidal waves, we waited. I timed them quite generously, I thought, then I went and peeked around the rhododendrons. They were at it still. I rejoined my wife, who was beginning to find my role in this highly comical. That hatch of flies would soon end and with it the evening rise. Why was I being so discreet for two such flagrant fornicators? Taking my wife by the hand I strode boldly out and down the path. The man's back was to us, hers was braced against the five-barred gate. He was hunched low, of necessity, and over his shoulder her face was visible, her head thrown back and her eyes closed. At the stage of his work, or rather his pleasure, to which he had arrived, or was arriving, he was oblivious to our approach. I observed in passing that he was gray-haired and getting bald on the crown, and also that rings glinted on the fingers with which she clasped him to her, one of them a gold wedding band. I opened the gate narrowly—

there was not room to open it wider—and my wife passed through. At that moment the lady opened her eyes and looked over her partner's shoulder and, seeing me, smiled like a cat being stroked and then let her eyes close again. I squeezed through the gate and down the stairs to the river, where I caught nothing.

Before dinner, to the bar (club license, membership open to guests upon payment of nominal subscription, good for length of stay) for a drink and curious for a closer look at our country copulatives of the afternoon. Passing the various tables and overhearing the conversations was like walking down an English street and hearing every house's telly tuned in on the same channel. Remarks sometimes rather muffled coming through thick military-style mustaches. "Jock Scott. Twenty-pound gut. Let it go past his snout, then lunged at it. Straight upstream taking the line clean down to the backing. Thought for a moment I'd foul-hooked him." Most of the gentlemen had dressed for dinner, the ladies all wore dinner gowns. Men in their sixties, women in their forties.

We never did see our siren of the garden gate again, nor did we recognize her partner (whose face neither of us had ever seen) until, on our way in to dinner en masse, my wife nudged me, nodded and whispered, "There. There's our man. I'd know that back anywhere." She had certainly spotted him. He could have been thus identified for arrest. But though unmistakable from the rear, Holloway, as he is known to all, or "poor Holloway," or "poor old Holloway," seen from the front, even allowing for his advantage of ten years over the rest, he being not much beyond fifty, looked as unlikely as any of them to be the Priapus we had seen perform earlier in the day. He was low-built, balding, and gray, as I noted earlier, getting paunchy, and, except for the ruddy tip of his nose, pallid in complexion. Nor did he look to me as if he quite belonged to those well-to-do whom Professor Jones says salmon fishing is the sport of. The guests at this place all know one another, being regulars who return year after year with the fish, and Holloway is treated by all as an old companion and equal. But I sensed that he was not. Between them and him I sensed a subtle but essential difference. Like the difference between one of Fortnum & Mason's old customers and one of its old salesclerks.

Wondering what sort of place this was where such a thing could happen as we had seen in the garden this afternoon, I played with the notion, whether he might not be on the payroll, like the tennis and riding instructor—an unadvertised attraction, of course: the salmon for the gentlemen, he for the salmon widows—until, as we were rising from our tables after dinner to leave, I saw him do a thing which, while it confirmed my suspicion that he was not to the sporting classes born (and one does not belong unless born to them), strongly suggested that he was not a member of the staff: he took from his

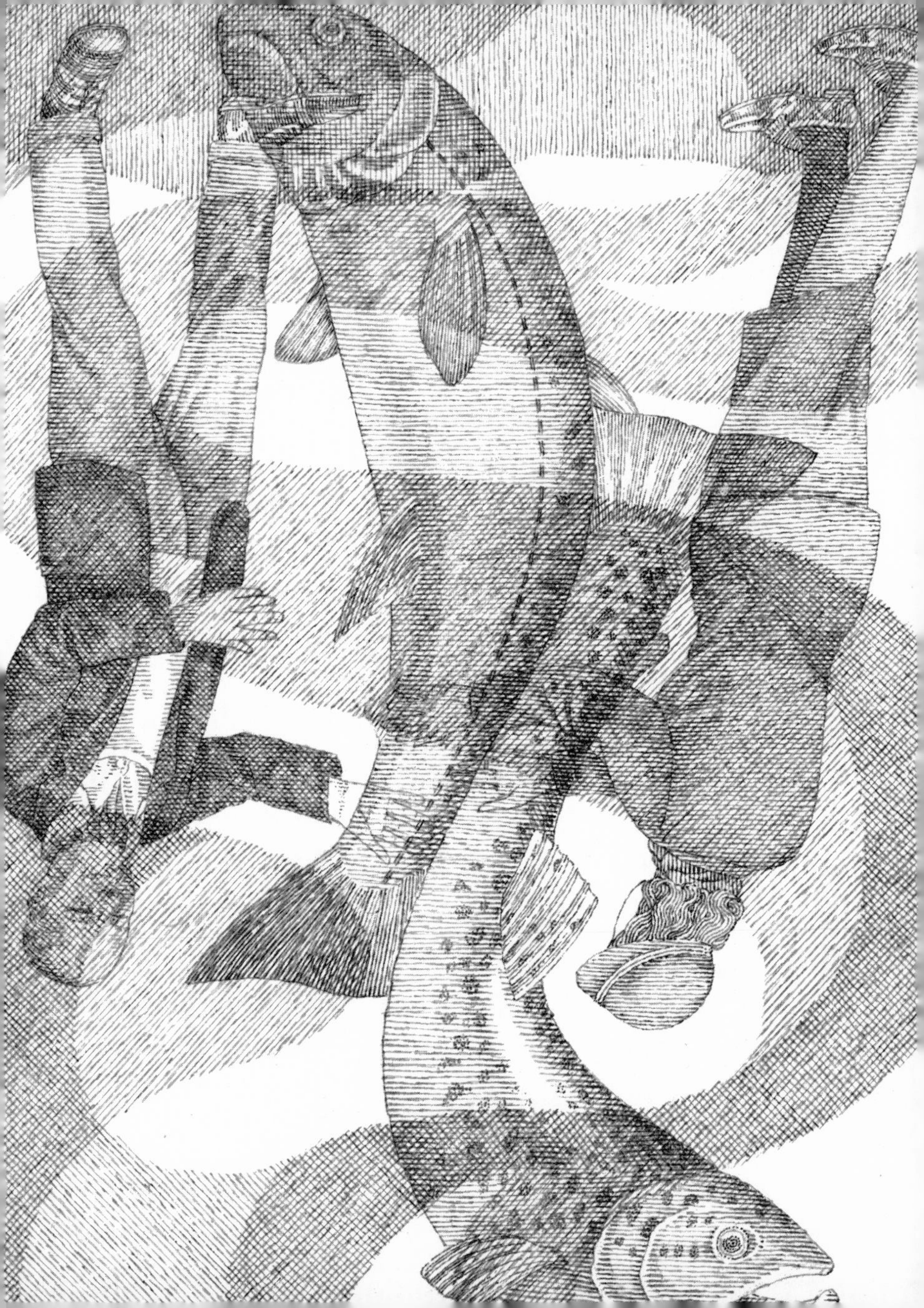

blazer pocket a ball-point pen and on the label of his wine bottle drew a line to mark the level of his consumption.

I forgot to note that he was unaccompanied and dined at a table for one. He was the only gentleman who dined alone, though some ladies did. These, I'm told, are widows—some of them quite youngish widows—who since the death of their angler husbands return regularly to The Redd for their holidays out of loyalty to their memories.

Even in Britain, where it is much more plentiful than it is in most countries, fresh salmon sells at the fishmonger's for fifteen shillings upward a pound. To quote Professor Jones, "The days are long past when apprentices in Britain petitioned against being given salmon to eat more than twice a week. The eating of salmon in Britain is now a luxury." And that fifteen-shilling salmon on sale at the fishmonger's is commercially caught salmon, from the coastal trawlers' nets. What a pound of salmon costs the sportsman who, like Mr. Porky Mitchell, has leased a beat on a river, or one who has traveled to Wales or Scotland and put up at some place like The Redd, and who may go for years without even hooking a fish, it is not possible to calculate: it must come close to the cost of those hummingbirds' tongues served at the feasts of the Roman emperors.

So when our fellow guest, Major Butler, instead of having that twenty-seven-pound cock he killed today boxed in ice and shipped home, as he might have done, had it served with his compliments to his fellow guests for dinner this evening, I thought this was a very generous gesture on his part until I tasted it. Salmon in Britain is poached ("in great numbers," runs the joke) in milk. The taste is describable. Poached milk.

At the table next to ours, with his lady, sat the old gentleman my wife met first, the one banging the barometer in the hall and predicting "they won't bite tomorrow," and after dinner we four drank coffee together in the lounge. Each spring for forty-two years, with time out for wars, Admiral Blakey has left the deep salt sea with the salmon and followed them up the Teme to The Redd, though for the last three of those years, on doctor's orders, he has not fished. This he tells me with quiet pride. But his wife: her smile looks forty-two years old. A Navy widow for most of the year, then on her holidays a salmon widow for forty-two years. I am reminded of the latest bit of lore I have learned from Professor Jones: "Those female salmon which for lack of opportunity or other reasons do not spawn, and which ultimately reabsorb their genital products (which fill their entire body cavity), are called *baggots,* or *rawners.*" I know I shall never cast fly over water again without seeing in memory Mrs. Blakey's baggotty smile, and feeling a twinge of complicity.

It was Holloway who led the general male exodus to bed following the nine-o'clock news on the telly. They had had a strenuous day on their beats (Holloway had had on his, I could vouch), and must be up and out early for another one tomorrow, besides,

"We're not as young as we were, are we, Tom?"—one of those remarks which you know the first time you hear it you're going to be hearing again, often. Many of them needed to be awakened in their armchairs and sent off to bed by their wives. Not Holloway, the first to retire, who has none. Watching him go, the Admiral shook his head so many times I decided he too had been behind a rhododendron watching this afternoon's tryst at the garden gate.

"Poor old Holloway," the Admiral at length sighed and said. It was then that I learned the name. "Poor bugger. You've got to admire perseverance like that."

I evinced interest.

"Fishes here. Fishes below here. Fishes above here," said the Admiral, sighing and shaking his head. "Fishes the Usk. The Severn. The Wye. Twenty years he's been fishing and never has caught a fish yet. Now that takes character. That is what I call sportsmanship. I mean to say, we're here to fish not to catch fish and all that—still, twenty years! I've been a keen angler in my time, but I do not believe I could have carried on with no more encouragement than that. Ah, but you should see the poor fellow on his beat! Can't handle his rod. Never knows where his fly will light, or if it will—he's got it caught in the trees more than he's got it in the water. Slips and falls while he's wading at least once a week and comes in half-drowned. Comes down with the grippe—that Teme water's cold this time of year—and we—the women, that is—have to take turns nursing him. I don't know how many times he's hooked himself on his back cast and had to be taken to the surgeon to have the fly cut out. Nasty thing, a three-ought Jock Scott in the earlobe. And yet the man carries on and keeps coming back for more. Never complains. Actually seems to enjoy himself here. Always cheerful. Always hopeful. Jolly good sport about it, too. Takes any amount of ribbing and takes it with a smile. Not many like that. It wants pluck."

"Never married?" I asked.

"Oh, no. No, no. Confirmed bachelor."

Though his days on the stream are over and he will never cast a Jock Scott again, the Admiral retires, at his wife's reminder, at half past nine. I last see him giving the barometer a final bang, then going slowly up the stairs shaking his head. Shortly afterward the bar comes alive for the night and Holloway is down again in time for the first round, the only unattached man. And while the veteran brothers of the angle alone upstairs in their beds sleep the simple sleep of Father Isaak Walton, poor old Holloway reigns over their wives like a pasha in his harem, or like a cock salmon among the hens on the spaw . . . .

The scream of a woman being murdered was what made me break off. I thought at the time it was the scream of a woman being murdered. Now five minutes later I don't know what to think. For I was alone when I dashed into the hallway in my pajamas, except for Holloway, also in his, who, in tiptoeing from the door of his bedroom to that of another one not his, gave me a wink in passing from which I inferred he was not going to the aid of a lady having her throat slowly slit.

wales, may 23

The woman screamed all night long at irregular intervals of from a quarter to half an hour, stopping only at daybreak. She was not being murdered, then, only tortured. Yet at breakfast this morning none of the other men (we anglers breakfast while our wives are still in bed) indicated by word or look that he had heard anything untoward in the night. They can't have slept through it. Impossible. Is this something known and accepted by all the regulars, one of those things one doesn't speak about? Would it not be in bad taste of me to mention what everyone else overlooks? Can poor Mr. Osborne, like Jane Eyre's Mr. Rochester, have a lunatic earlier wife attached to the wall by a chain somewhere in an outlying wing who howls by night? If so, I wouldn't want to be the one to draw attention to it.

I felt conspicuous enough already, dressed as I would dress to go fishing back home, in old blue jeans, a blue work shirt I once wore to paint a red barn, and my Brooklyn Dodgers baseball cap, while my fellow guests wore Harris Tweed jackets, drill-cord riding breeches, tweed hats from Lock's, and neckties.

After breakfast—eggs with salmon—we drew lots for our beats on the river. It had begun to rain in the night so we all set off in rain gear—I in my plastic mac—over our waders and hip boots, and with our pipes turned down. I speak not only for myself when I say that our turned-down pipes, with rain dripping from them, perfectly symbolized our spirits. A north wind was blowing, and "when the wind is in the north, then the fisherman goeth not forth"; Admiral Blakey, with forty-two years of barometer-banging behind him, had foretold that they wouldn't be biting today; and the rain was coming down in spouts. Some of us might have turned back, but for the presence of Holloway in our midst. That shamed us for our faintheartedness. Gaff in hand, like a bishop's crook, he set an example for anglers everywhere to follow. If he, with his dismal record, could carry on undismayed, we could, we must.

The rain had washed all the hubcaps clean and bright and the peacock found himself surrounded this morning by fresh rivals.

One fishes for salmon in waters one may oneself safely drink, waters of the clearest crystal—when not in spate, that is. For the salmon is the most fastidious of fish and does not tolerate the least pollution. His sensitivity to human wastes and to the wastes of manufacture kills him or else drives him away in disgust.

The Teme is a spring river. That is to say, its salmon return to spawn in the spring. Other rivers are fall rivers; their salmon return in the fall. But all salmon spawn in the fall, including those that come back into the rivers in the spring. And while they wait, some of them for up to nine months, they fast.

Can it really be true that salmon, such voracious eaters in the ocean, once they reenter freshwater, fast? Fast absolutely? Fast to the death? All salmon? All salmon fast, absolutely, and all but a few of them fast to the death. Not much is certain about this little-known though much-studied fish, but that much is. Never a trace of food has been found in the dissected insides of one, not even those known to have been in the river for periods of up to nine months. People have always found this hard to credit, and it was once widely believed that none was ever caught with food in its stomach because they vomited on being hooked. Not so. They quit eating.

Then why will they—sometimes—strike at a fisherman's fly? Or a shrimp (prawn, they say here)? Or a fly tied to imitate a prawn? Or a minnow? Or a spinner made to imitate a minnow? Or a gob of worms on a hook? Why, indeed? To this, the oldest and most intriguing question about the salmon, you will not find the answer even in Professor Jones's book (about which I am beginning to feel as the little girl felt about the one she was assigned to review, and reviewed so pithily, to wit: This book tells me more about penguins than I care to know). Professor Jones speculates that it may be done out of irritability, and anyone who has ever seen a salmon (I am thinking now of the male salmon) taken from the spawning bed can easily see why he should think so. The salmon at this stage looks irritable. In fact, he looks downright ferocious, deformed by his single-minded obsession with sex.

What does the salmon live on? Love; that's the obvious answer. But he's not living, he's dying. This is going to be the death of him. He's eating himself alive: all that stored-up deep-sea fat, and not just fat, muscle, too. As he lies in the pool doing nothing, not even eating, from March until September, his idle mind on evil thoughts, his disused alimentary organs shrink and shrivel and practically disappear to make room for the gonads that swell and swell and swell until that is all he—or she—is inside. Meanwhile the silver sheen he came in with from the sea turns dull, and his meat turns red and kipper. The male grows a growth, called a kype, on the tip of his underjaw, forcing it away from the upper one, which also develops a hook, giving to his expression a rapacious snarl.

When the time comes for the salmon to spawn—when the female is "running ripe"—after a brief courtship in the quiet of the pools, they move upstream into the swift water. It is there that the eggs must be laid because they require for their incubation constant percolation of the water through the gravel surrounding them in their redd.

It is as impossible for a salmon as it is for you or me to tell whether another salmon is a male or a female just by looking. For much of their lives they don't care. When the time comes to care the salmon have a way of telling who's who, or rather, who's what. A salmon sidles up to another salmon and quivers. If the other fish quivers in response then it's a male like himself, but if it turns over on its side and begins flapping its tail on the river bottom, then it's a match.

When she is ready to spawn the female salmon begins "cutting." That is, flapping her tail against the river bottom so hard she digs a hole in the gravel. With her anal fin she keeps feeling the hole until she is satisfied with the depth of it. It must be about a foot deep to suit her. When she is satisfied with it she crouches over the hole. Thereupon the male salmon joins her. He draws alongside her without touching. He begins to quiver eagerly. She gapes. He gapes.

For lunch today my wife was served *croquettes de saumon.* I had one of my old friend Mitchell's meat pies in a box put up for me by the hotel. For me, Admiral Blakey's glum prediction proved accurate and I returned fishless and as wet as a fish myself. But for two of my fellow guests, I heard with an envious heart, a game smile, and a sinking appetite, the day yielded salmon of large size.

Again all night long every few minutes that woman screamed, and again we were the only ones to notice it. Only long familiarity with it can explain the self-composure of our fellow guests. That, or the well-known British self-discipline. As for me, I don't think I could ever get used to it. It curdles my American blood. The first time it happened I bolted from bed and into the hall again. I was still there listening for it to come again when poor old Holloway emerged from his room and went tiptoeing past in his pajamas. He gave me his wink, and, in my amazement, I believe I may have returned it.

The mating of salmon, concluded:

It is concluded, all but. That was it. A union without contact between the partners, a crouch, a quiver, a mutual gape. It not only doesn't look like much fun, from the human point of view; when you remember what a long way they've come, past what snares and ambushes, over almost insuperable obstacles, how they have gone hungry and grown disfigured, and knowing as you do that it will prove fatal, it seems pitifully unworthy of the trouble. A cheat. There is worse to come.

Friends, if you have tears prepare to shed them now. I know I nearly did when I got to the chapter in Professor Jones's book in which in cold ichthyological prose he relates the betrayal, the ignominy which now overtakes this grand fish.

For the sake of this moment the salmon has swum maybe fifteen hundred miles through nobody knows what perils of the deep. He has—and he is one of the few that have—eluded the trawlers' nets and the fishmonger's cold slate slab, or, more ignoble end still, the cannery. He will not have come this far without having felt the barb and fought free of some of the many Jock Scotts and Black Doses and Silver Doctors dangled temptingly before him. He has leaped twelve-foot-high falls. He has survived gill maggots, fin worms, leeches, boils, white rot, white spot, gill catarrh, fungus, carp lice, sea lice. For this he has fasted, for this he will die. Now he is about to achieve fulfillment of his desire. The female has finished her cutting. With her anal fin she has felt out the redd and found it satisfactory. He now hangs alongside her, quivering eagerly. She crouches. She gapes. He gapes. She sheds some of her eggs, about nine hundred of them. Now begins for him the release of some of that pent-up milt which in two ripe testes fills his entire body. And from out of nowhere, more often than not, some impudent little Holloway of a parr darts in and discharges his tuppence worth! This little delinquent may be no more than four inches long. *He* has swum no seas. *He* has leapt no falls. *He* has foiled no Englishman armed with two-handed rod of split bamboo. He has been nowhere, done nothing, cheeky little imp. Yet this little love thief, this mischievous minnow scarcely out of his caviarhood, has just cuckolded a cock salmon some two hundred times his size, right under his nose, so to speak, and has cheated him of his paternity as well; for puny as they are, they are potent, these precocious parr.

But then the old cock was once a parr himself and played the same trick on his elders and betters in his youth.

After shedding her eggs the female salmon moves a little ways upstream and begins cutting another redd. She is killing two birds with one stone. For the gravel raised in the cutting of this new redd is carried downstream by the current and covers the eggs she has just deposited.

Back at the hotel, today for lunch there were *timbales de saumon.*

wales, may 27

The mystery of the woman who screams in the night is solved. My wife finally mustered the courage to speak of it to one of the other ladies. It's the peahen.

It's the mating season for them, too, and peahens, it seems, do that at this time. My God, said my wife, what does her mate do to her to make her scream like that? Or not do to her to make her scream like that, said the other lady, vain, self-infatuated creature; had you thought, my dear, of that?

And so life for a salmon begins not in but under a river, where, along with eight or nine hundred of his brother and sister caviar, his mother has buried him. That will have been in the fall. Next spring he hatches out, though remaining inside the redd.

At first the infant salmon is nothing more than a drop of egg yolk with a tail and a pair of bug eyes. This little tadpole is called an alevin.

If he is not found and eaten by another salmon or a trout or washed away in a spate of the river or stepped on by a cow or a wading angler, the alevin, after about a month, by which time his egg sac has been consumed, comes out of the redd into the river a proper little fish, a fingerling or a fry, at which change his actuarial table dips even more sharply.

For now he is the prey not only of his cannibal kin and of his cousins the trout, but also of pike, perch, chub, eels, ducks, swans, herons, and cormorants, and of droughts, for the fingerling is even more sensitive than he will be when he grows up to any rise in the water's temperature.

When the young salmon grows to be longer than a man's finger then it is no longer a fingerling. It is then a parr—here in Wales, a sil; in other localities (I am indebted to Professor Jones for this list of delightful names): a pink, a samlet, a peal, a branlin, a skegger (so Walton called them), a locksper, a skirling, a laspring, and a samson.

It's about this time that a salmon finds out whether it's a he or a she. If a she, there is nothing to do but be patient and wait; if a he, then the fun has begun, at the old cocks' expense.

The salmon remains a parr for two years, spending the whole of the time in his native pool or near it, growing to be about four or five inches long and to weigh about as many ounces. Then the salmon goes to sea, a smolt now. After just one year there it may be a foot and a half long and weigh three pounds or more. If it stays there four years it will come back four or five feet long and weighing forty or forty-five pounds. The salmon is a grilse when it returns to spawn, a kelt after having done so.

Thus one salmon in his time plays many parts, his acts being seven ages: egg, alevin, fingerling or fry, parr, smolt, grilse (cock or hen), and, last scene of all, which ends this strange eventful history, kelthood and mere oblivion, sans teeth, sans eyes, sans taste, sans everything.

Unless it be a hen and she turns out an old maid, and then she has another: baggott, or rawner.

Lunch today: *quenelles de saumon.*

wales, may 28

Every time I'm just about to doze off to sleep the peahen screams. What can he be doing to her?

In the evening, after dinner, before trooping off to bed, we anglers attend to our tackle.

Rather than disjoint our rods at the end of the day only to have to joint them again early on the morrow, we stand them jointed in a rack inside the ground-floor gentlemen's loo (as it's called here), to the right just inside the front door, opposite the barometer. There too we leave our gaffs and our rain gear, our muddy boots and waders, and there after dinner we go to get our reels and unwind our wet lines to hang them out to dry overnight. The open but covered loggia provides an ideal place for this, and we stretch them between brass hooks in the walls. Then those—and I am one of them—who favor knotted tapered leaders (or casts) over the knotless ones which are sold by the tackle shops, convinced that they sink better—and a leader must sink, for otherwise it casts a shadow, and nothing frightens a fish like a shadow—those, I say, who think as I think, sit snipping from their spools lengths of monofilament nylon of graduated gauges and joining them together with good blood knots pulled tight. Meanwhile others of us tie flies out of feathers and fur and tinsel. This done, we hone the barbs of our hooks, which from striking against gravel and stones in the stream all day have become blunted. Many a good fish has gotten away thanks to a blunt hook, and it is Admiral Blakey's judgment that the logbook (more on this later), in which not once in twenty years does Holloway's name appear, might tell a different story if instead of making a bloody fool of himself among the ladies after dinner he spent his time sharpening his hooks. Then we oil our reels and we patch any holes or rips in our waders and boots and then we yawn and we recall the strenuous day we have had on the beat and tell one another that we must be up and out early for another one tomorrow and we remind ourselves that we are not as young as we once were and we excuse ourselves to the ladies and then we go up to bed.

Today for lunch there was *soufflé de saumon.*

There is a gap of a day in my diary.

I came in wet and fishless late yesterday afternoon, to find in my bed, where she had spent the day, going without lunch, my own salmon widow. The mood of the place and the season was upon her. On my approaching near and giving a quiver, she responded by showing a readiness to spawn. Indeed, she was running ripe; as for me, I grew a kype on the spot. We passed up supper, fasting instead, and came down late this morning, feeling and looking rather kelt.

If a wink can be said to be broad, Holloway's was to me at cocktail time this evening.

Is it a leftover bit of old sympathetic magic—drink your enemy's blood, eat his flesh, and thereby acquire the power to think as he thinks before he thinks it—that lies behind this unbroken diet of salmon?

Three years have gone by since Admiral Blakey last felt the thrill of a taut line, and for the last couple of years before that his catch was small as the limit of the reach of his arm was exceeded by his progressive farsightedness, and the growing smallness of fishhooks' eyes forced the old angler to set forth in the morning with his Jock Scott tied on his leader for him and to have to abandon his sport and trudge home if through misadventure he lost it and could find no younger brother of the fraternity along the stream bank to tie on another one for him.

Now that his angling is ended, the Admiral's evenings, like the Admiral's days, are spent in catching, or rather re-catching fish, in memory. Admiral Blakey's memory for fish is naturally retentive, and this is in contrast to his memory for any and everything else. His wife must prompt him whenever he tries to recall any of their children's Christian names, but he can and, what is worse, does tell you the weight of, down to the odd ounces, and the weather, wind, and water conditions attendant upon the killing of every fish he ever killed in his life. And you can be man or woman indifferently for the Admiral to tell you this; he no more knows the sex of his listener than a salmon past quivering knows who, that is to say what, he is communicating with. The man's talk, like the menu of this hotel, is always the same. He has caught a lot of fish in his time, and has more stories to tell about them—and the ones that got away—than a hen salmon has eggs.

The Blakeys have four children. He had a little trouble recalling exactly how many there were of them, but she reminded him with such positiveness I could not but think the number corresponded to the number of their conjugal embraces, lifetime. Despite myself, under the influence of this place I tried to imagine one of those embraces. The most I could conjure up was something with about as much intimacy of contact as that between the cock salmon and the hen. I pictured the two of them lying side by side without touching, and after a while gaping together.

I could never in the course of our acquaintance—short, to be sure, though it got to seem very long before it ended—form any image of the admiral in Admiral Blakey. Here was a man who had risen to a post of supreme command in a profession fabled in story and song, and it all seemed to have passed over him without leaving a trace, supplanted by the sport he had pursued. He never reminisced about his naval adventures, his imagery was not drawn from ships or the sea, his talk was as un-nautical as a cotton farmer's. He had but his one topic, and had I had the rights of those bygone apprentices, I should certainly have petitioned against being served it more than twice a week. True, I had my chance to study Admiral Blakey only while at The Redd during spawning season; of what he is like during the rest, which is the greater part, of the year, I know no more than any of us knows of the salmon's life in the sea. He may get it all out of his system during his one month here and on leaving have no more interest left in angling than a kelt has in sex, for all I know about it. If this be so, however, I fear it may leave the old gentleman quite spent, with no topic for talk at all, and to this fear I am prompted by the unbroken silence which at table, as well as at all other times, reigns between him and his wife.

The Admiral's memory for fish, as I said, is naturally good. But in telling my wife that the wind was south-southwest at seven miles an hour, the barometer at 29.44 inches and rising, the water low and clear, that he was using a 2/0 Durham Ranger on a ten-pound gut when at 4:42 p.m., June 10, 1929, after a fight lasting twenty-one minutes, he killed a hen salmon measuring thirty-four and one half inches and weighing thirty-two pounds six and three-quarter ounces, the Admiral is assisted in the details by a promptbook here in the hotel. This document, in eighty-nine volumes, one for each year going back to 1881, is a record of every fish ever caught here by the hotel's every guest, with all attendant circumstances. This is the book in which, guest though he has been for twenty of those years, poor old Holloway's name never once appears, and neither will poor old Humphrey's, it begins to seem pretty certain. These volumes provide the Admiral his reading matter. He spends the day poring over them and chuckling to himself, and he is only too happy to share his pleasure with any lady who happens along. In the current one, kept not in the bookcase along with the rest but out on a table in the salon, I had seen, despite all my contrivances not to see them, my more fortunate—more skillful, should I not say?—fellow anglers taking turns making their entries for the day while digesting their salmon in the evening.

This evening I was perusing the volume for 1934, marveling again at the British national sense of honor that would entrust the keeping of a fishing log to the fishermen themselves, when my wife got off the Admiral's hook and he joined me.

"Nineteen thirty-four!" said the Admiral, and over

his watery eyes spread that mist of happy recollection which the mention of any one of the last forty-two years excluding the very last five can produce. "The eighteenth of June, 1934! There's a day I shall always remember, and yet you won't find it noted in the book there. I'd drawn number six as my beat that day. A rainy day it was, barometer at thirty inches and steady, the wind out of the west at nine miles an hour, gusting up to fourteen. My rod was a Leonard, thirteen feet long, mounted with a 6/0 Hardy reel. My line was a King Eider silk, backed with three hundred feet of thirty-pound backing. My cast tapered from .060 inches in the butt to .022 in the tippet. I was fishing a 2/0 Silver Wilkinson, having observed in the river quantities of chub minnows which that pattern in that size most closely imitated. It was precisely twelve noon by the clock in nearby Llanblfchfpstdwwy Church tower when I got a strike that very nearly tore the rod from my grip. This fish behaved in a most uncommon manner from the start. As you know, Humphrey, once hooked, a salmon can be generally relied upon to run in the direction in which he invariably faces owing to rheotaxis, also known as rheotropism, namely, upstream. This fish never once made an upstream run; he went steadily, and at a steady speed approximating that of the current, downriver. Within moments he had taken my line and three-quarters of my backing. I put all the pressure on him I dared, giving him the butt of the rod and straining the gut to just under breaking point. There was no turning or raising him. Straight downriver hugging the bed he went as though determined to get back into the sea. I could regain not an inch of my line and I dared not let him have an inch more than he had already. There was but one tactic to adopt: wade with him downstream keeping pressure on him constantly until he should tire. We were, as I said, near Llanblfchfpstdwwy Church, on beat six, and the time was precisely twelve noon. At half past two we passed the ruins of Cwffd-nant-Bwlch Abbey, and I still had regained none of my line. This of course had taken us through beats seven, eight, and nine, where in succession my good friends the Reverend Smythe-Prestwick, may he rest in peace, Colonel Watson, and Mr. Finchley, had very obligingly withdrawn their lines and themselves from the water to allow my fish and me to pass through. Though my rod was bowed into a hoop, the fish swam on untiringly. I began to think perhaps I had foul-hooked him. We went by and through the villages of Mmfcwmmr, Upper Llndwrtfynydd-ar-y-bryn, Lower Llndwrtfynydd-ar-y-bryn, and Bwlch-ddû, and were passing The 23rd Royal Welch Fusiliers—that's a pub—some five miles from our point of contact, when at last I felt him begin to weaken. I now began to reel in steadily, and within another half-mile I got my first sight of him. Or, rather, them. For to my astonishment and delight, I discovered that I had got on not one but two large fish, one to each of the fly's two hooks. A most uncommon occurrence even in the life of a very experienced angler, and so I resolved to have them mounted, side by side and cheek by jowl, sharing the fly. At last I brought them to gaff, and at seven thirty-four p.m. I lifted from the water the biggest pair of waders I believe I ever saw in my life. I said to myself at the time that the man who came out of them would scale sixteen stone. And I was proved right when two days later my good friend Colonel Watson, fishing beat number two, hooked him on a 4/0 Black Dose."

At dinner this evening, or rather at dinner's end, Holloway, after marking the label of his wine bottle, came over to the Blakeys' table.

"Well, Admiral," he said, with a wink at me over the old angler's head. "Well, Mrs. Blakey. It's been lovely seeing you both again. Lovely. I shall look forward to seeing you both again next year. Good-bye."

"Good-bye," said the Admiral.

"Good-bye," said Mrs. Blakey.

"He's going, then, is he?" said the Admiral, shaking his head sympathetically at Holloway's departing back.

"No, dear. We are."

"Oh, yes. To be sure. So we are."

wales, june 1

Fishing demands faith. Faith like St. Peter's when the Lord bade him cast his hook into the water and catch a fish for money to pay tribute to Caesar. To catch a fish you have got to have faith that the water you are fishing in has got fish in it, and that you are going to catch one of them. You still may not catch anything; but you certainly won't if you don't fish your best, and you won't do this without faith to inspire you to do it. You won't approach the water carefully. You won't study the water carefully. You won't cast carefully. You won't fish out your cast;

to do this, patience is required, and patience is grounded on faith. You won't fish each stretch of the water thoroughly before giving up on it and moving to the next stretch. The satisfactions of a day's fishing are deep; and just as deep on a day when you don't catch a fish; but unless you keep faith that you are going to catch a fish that day, then fishing seems a waste—a waste of time, money, effort, and, most depressing, a waste of spirit. Faith and faith alone can guard the fisherman against a demon of which he is particularly the prey, the demon of self-irony, from acquiescence in the opinion of the ignorant that he is making a fool of himself. Few things can make a man feel more fully a man than fishing, if he has got faith; nothing can make a man feel more fully a fool if he has not got faith.

After nine days of fishing the Teme without once getting a nibble I had lost my faith. Not my faith that there were fish in the river. They were there, all right. With my own eyes I had seen, and with my own knife and fork had eaten, a miraculous draught

of Teme fishes. The fish were there; I had lost my faith that I was going to catch one of them, and my cup of self-irony ranneth over. I cast and I cast and I cast again with that big heavy rod, I beat those waters until my wrists swelled and stiffened and ached me all night long while that peahen screamed, and I marveled how Holloway could make shift to keep on at this drudgery even as a camouflage to the pleasures that he returns here to possesse (*sic*) himself of.

Then this afternoon, defeated, deflated, and dejected, heedless in my approach, clomping along the bank in my heavy, hobnailed boots and casting my shadow I cared not where—the first shadow I had been able to cast since coming into Wales—I came to a bend in the river where the undercutting of the bank by the current made a pool and into this pool I did not cast my Green Highlander, I dismissed it there, with leave to go where it would on its own; I didn't care if I never saw it again.

The big fly lighted at the head of the pool near

the opposite bank and quickly sank. Absently I watched the line swing out into the current. I saw it stop. I was hooked on a snag. In my mood this was all I needed and, lowering my rod I grasped the line to break the fly off, disjoint my rod, and go home. But I was using a heavy leader, one bigger in the tippet than any leader I had ever used in my trout fishing back home was in the butt, and it would not break. I gave another angry yank, whereupon my line began to move. I thought I had dislodged the snag from the riverbed and was still hooked to it, until I reflected that an object dislodged from the riverbed would move downstream with the current, not upstream. I had had a strike and had struck back without even knowing it and had hooked the biggest fish of my life.

I reeled in the slack line and raised my rod. He was still on. His run was short. He had gone to the bottom to sulk and I could not budge him. When I put the butt of the rod to him and saw the rod bow and heard the line tighten and felt his size and strength, a sense of my unworthiness came over me and I was smitten with guilt and contrition.

I didn't deserve to land this fish. Fishing without faith, I had done nothing as it ought to be done. He had hooked himself—I just happened to be holding the other end of the line. I pictured him lying there on the riverbed in all his unseen silvery majesty. How mysterious and marvelous a creature he was! I thought how far he had come to get here and of the obstacles he had braved and bested. While keeping pressure on him with my rod held high, I thought of the towering falls he had leapt, driven by the overmastering urge to breed and perpetuate his kind. And here was I about to kill him before he could achieve the hard-won consummation of his desire. It was the king of fish I was about to assassinate. I felt like a cur.

How often in books published by the most reputable houses, with editors who verify their authors' every assertion, had I read with soul dilated of one of that greathearted breed of dry-fly ascetics who, every time he caught Old Methuselah, the venerable yard-long brown trout of Potts' Pool, put him back—until under cover of darkness one night a clod armed with nightcrawlers and a clothesline unblushingly yanked Old Methuselah out and brained him with a car jack and the magic of Potts' Pool departed forever. I said to my soul now, I won't gaff him. A fish as noble as this deserved a better end than poached in milk or jellied in aspic and garnished with blobs of mayonnaise. I could see myself already, this evening at the hotel, smiling a wistful smile when my fat and fish-fed fellow guests commiserated with me on my day after penning their entries in the logbook. For when I had fought the fish into submission, when I had mastered his valiant spirit with my own even more valiant one, when he turned over and lay floating belly-up at my feet, I would carefully extract the hook and hold him right-side-up and facing into the current until he got his breath back, and then I would bid him go, finned friend, go, my brother, and do not slink in shame, go in pride and intact, gallant old warrior, go, and eschew Green Highlanders.

I would like hell.

I sometimes return a little fish to the water, but I leave it to those knights of the outdoors who contribute articles to the sporting magazines, and who catch so many more of them than I ever will, to put back big ones.

I raised my rod so high it quivered; still the fish clung stubbornly to his spot. Every once in a while the fish would give a little shake of his head, transmitted to me through the taut line, as if to test whether he still had me hooked. I held on. He would let minutes pass, then would wallow and shake his head as if he were enjoying this. It was like having a bull by the ring in his nose and being afraid to let go of it. At one point, resting one of my wrists by holding the end of the rod between my legs, I had a moment of wild wonder at myself, at the question I had just asked myself: did I really want to catch a fish this big? Heretical thought for a fisherman; yet I could not relate this to fishing as I knew it. I was used to exulting when I netted a fourteen-inch trout weighing a pound and a quarter. Now my hopes had been overfulfilled. Truth was, I was scared of the sea monster that I had—or that had me—on the line and couldn't get off.

After fifteen minutes my fish began to move. The drag on my reel was set to just under the breaking strength of my leader, yet he stripped line from the reel with a speed that made the ratchet buzz like a doorbell. I was not wading but was on the bank; now I began to run along the bank—I should say, I was dragged along it. When he had gone a hundred and fifty yards upstream—with me giving him precious line at one point so I could negotiate a fence stile, then sprinting, in hobnailed hip boots, to regain it—he braked, shook his head, then turned and sped downstream a hundred and fifty yards, taking me back over the fence stile. I still had not seen him, and the slant of my line in the water told me I was not going to see him for some time to come. He was deep, hugging the river bottom.

For forty-five minutes he kept this up—I clambered over that fence stile six times from both directions—growing an inch longer and a pound heavier in my mind—my wrists, too—each minute. When he quit it was not gradually, it was all at once, as if he had fought with every ounce of his strength and all his determination up to the very end. I stepped into the shallow water at the edge, and, gaining line, began reeling him toward me. Even his unresisting weight strained my big rod. Ten feet from where I stood his dorsal fin broke water. It was three feet back from where my line entered the water; three feet back from it the tip of his tail broke the surface. My mouth was dry with desire. I gaffed him. Or rather, I made a pass at him with the gaff, nicked him, he turned, lunged, and was gone. The line snapped back and wound itself around the rod like a vine. My leader had parted at one of the blood-knots I had so tightly tied. There was something detestable in the very shape—curly, coiled, kinky—of the end I was left holding. Imagine a pig the size of a penny and he would have a tail just like that.

I smiled wistfully, all right, that evening at the hotel when the others, penning their entries in the logbook, commiserated with me on my day.

ross-on-wye, june 2

At lunch today—*mousse de saumon*—Holloway drained his bottle of wine. He is moving on further upstream for his annual stay at another fisherman's hotel to try his rotten luck there. Poor old Holloway! You've got to admire perseverance like that. We also were leaving this afternoon, also leaving behind in the logbook no record of our stay. But, with the wind east-southeast and the barometer at twenty-nine inches and falling, using a Green Highlander on a 2/0 hook, I had had one get away that would easily have gone to thirty-five—what am I saying?—forty-five pounds! Up to the end Holloway was still trying. He will be making the spawning run up the Teme and stopping at The Redd again next spring, his twenty-first. The last I saw of Holloway he was teaching a willing pupil, young Mrs. Bradley, whose old husband drew a rather distant beat on the river this morning, a lesson in the gentle art of angling. Which, as Walton's Piscator instances in support of his contention that ours is an art of high esteem, was how Anthony and Cleopatra also whiled away their leisure moments.

And the poor salmon, on whom love seems so hard—do all of them die after spawning? Nine-tenths of them do; of those that survive it, nine-tenths are hens. Professor Jones offers no explanation of why so many more of the males die than the females. At the risk of anthropomorphizing, I would suggest it's from shame at being so often and so openly cuckolded by those pesky parr; except that there is no evidence to indicate that the cock salmon know anything more about what is going on right under their own tails than the anglers did who came to angle for them at The Redd. The widowed hens return, the way we have just come today, to the sea, and there grow fat and sleek and silvery again and then return to spawn another time. Some durable old girls make it back twice more. A few old rips make it back three more times.

A Note on the Type

This book was set in Monotype Bulmer. This distinguished type face is a competent recutting of a type long famous in the history of English printing that was designed and cut by William Martin about 1790 for William Bulmer of the Shakespeare Press. In design, it is all but a modern face, with vertical stress, sharp differentiation between the thick and thin strokes, and nearly flat serifs. The decorative italic shows the influence of Baskerville ; Martin was John Baskerville's pupil.

The book was composed by Westcott & Thomson, Inc., Philadelphia, Pennsylvania. It was printed by Universal Lithographers, Timonium, Maryland, and bound by L. H. Jenkins, Richmond, Virginia. Typography and binding design by Betty Anderson.